JACK JOUETT

PORTRAIT OF AN AMERICAN HERO

BY **Martha J. Hutcherson** • Illustrated BY **Rebecca B. Blair**

BENJAMIN PRESS

BENJAMIN PRESS

135 North Second Street
Danville, Kentucky 40422 USA
www.benjaminpress.com
800.765.2139

Hutcherson, Martha J.
Jack Jouett : portrait of an American hero / by Martha J. Hutcherson ; illustrations by Rebecca B. Blair.
ISBN 978-0-9836106-4-9

Printed in Canada

Jack Jouett House Historic Site
255 Craig's Creek Road
Versailles, KY 40383
859.873.7902

Information and teacher guide may be found at
www.jouetthouse.org

JACK JOUETT

PORTRAIT OF AN AMERICAN HERO

BENJAMIN PRESS

Hello! My name is Matthew Jouett. Many years ago I painted portraits of famous people. I've always been sorry I never painted a portrait of my father, Captain Jack Jouett. He was famous for helping to change the history of our country — he and his spunky mare named Sally.

His adventure began in Virginia during the Revolutionary War. We Americans needed money and supplies to fight the British in our struggle for independence. Our leaders and lawmakers gathered in Charlottesville to discuss these problems with Governor Thomas Jefferson.

On the night of June 3, 1781, my father was staying 40 miles away at the Cuckoo Tavern. The heat of the day lasted into the night, so he decided to sleep outside underneath a big elm tree.

During the night, Father awoke to the clatter of hoof beats.

Peeking around the tree, he saw mounted British soldiers led by the fierce Colonel Tarleton. They were trotting down the road toward Charlottesville where our leaders were meeting.

Father realized that Tarleton was planning to arrest them all!

Father knew he was the only person who could stop the British from carrying out their plan. He quickly pulled on his leather boots, settled his tri-cornered hat on his head, picked up his pistol, and whistled for Sally, who was grazing in a nearby paddock.

"Sally," whispered Father, "we must get to Charlottesville before the British! The American leaders need time to escape!"

Father and Sally set out on the main road, stopping around midnight at an overlook. Gazing down through the trees, Father saw Tarleton's men resting from the heat, their guns shining in the moonlight.

There was just one way to get ahead of the British. Father guided Sally onto an old logging trail, made narrow with overgrown trees and shrubs, and slippery with mud. Father's coat was torn, and thorns slashed his face, hands, and arms. Soon he and Sally were covered with mud and sweat.

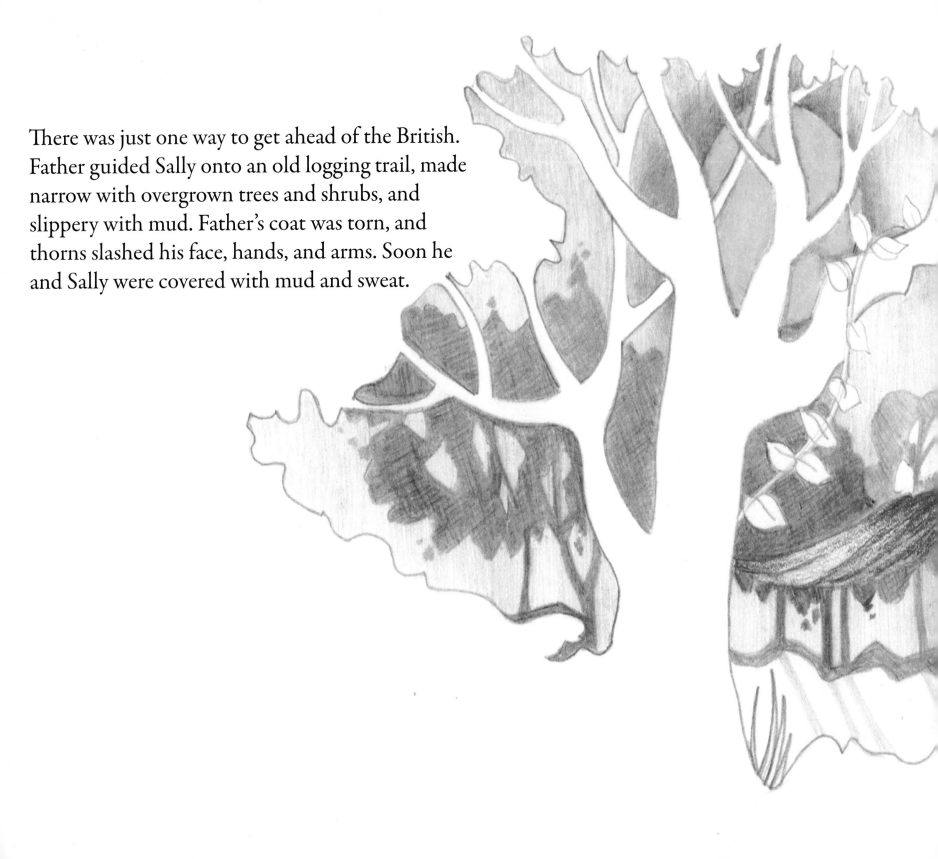

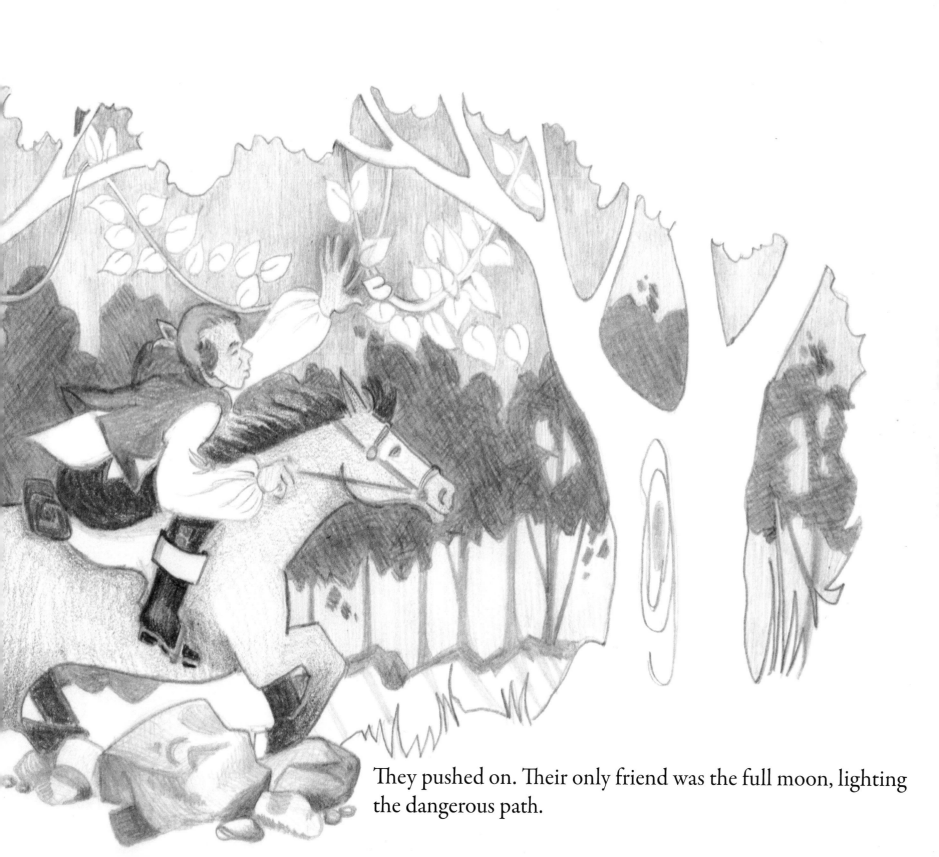

They pushed on. Their only friend was the full moon, lighting the dangerous path.

Deep in the woods, Father stopped at a creek to rest Sally and bathe their wounds. They had barely resumed their journey when Sally tripped on a wild grapevine. Horse and rider tumbled to the ground. They rose bruised and shaken to continue on their way.

Before daybreak, the exhausted pair finally came in sight of Monticello, the beautiful hilltop home of Governor Jefferson. Charlottesville was only two miles away. Father breathed a sigh of relief. He and Sally had outrun old Tarleton!

What my father didn't know was that Tarleton had made two other stops along the way. He captured and burned a wagon train of supplies on its way to our Continental Army.

Tarleton also stopped at Castle Hill Farm, the home of Dr. Thomas Walker, where he demanded breakfast. He discovered that a member of the Continental Congress was visiting the farm and took that man captive.

Back at Monticello, Father rapped on the door. Governor Jefferson was shocked by his appearance. Father's clothes were bloodstained, and he had a gash over one eye. He told his story quickly and then set off on Sally to warn the lawmakers in nearby Charlottesville.

He arrived at the Swan Tavern, where many of the leaders were staying. Father knew the tavern well — my grandfather owned it — and a trusted servant hurried to take care of the faithful Sally while my father raced inside. My grandmother tended to his wounds, but only after Father explained his urgent business to the lawmakers.

"Tarleton is close behind me," he exclaimed. "You must leave town immediately!"

The lawmakers decided to meet the next week in Staunton, about 40 miles west. Leaving breakfast on the table, they rushed out the door.

Grandfather's old friend, General Edward Stevens, was recovering from a battle wound and could not move so quickly. He put on a shabby cloak, climbed onto an old horse, and rode slowly out of town.

A few minutes later, my father appeared, dressed in an officer's red coat complete with gold braid and a plumed hat. Sitting astride a fresh horse, he calmly awaited the arrival of Tarleton and his men.

The British appeared in the distance. Glimpsing the red uniform, Tarleton believed Father was an important American officer and chased after him, allowing General Stevens to escape. The tired British horses were no match for Father's new mount, so he easily outran them.

Although the British captured a few escaping lawmakers, including frontiersman Daniel Boone, they failed in their plan to seize the important leaders of the Revolution.

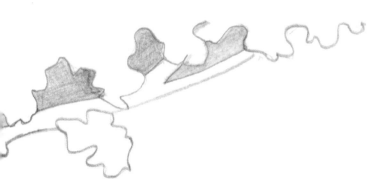

And so my father, Captain Jack Jouett, became a real hero! At their meeting in Staunton, the lawmakers voted to present him with a fine sword and a pair of gleaming pistols because he had so bravely aided America's war for independence.

After America won the Revolutionary War, Father moved to Kentucky. He settled near a place known as Harrodsburg. Father married his childhood sweetheart Sally Robards, for whom his remarkable mare was named. After several years they moved to Woodford County, where they built a home and had twelve children.

Father was elected to the legislature and helped Kentucky become a state separate from Virginia. He became a successful farmer and horse breeder. Throughout his life, my father served his state and nation. He earned the respect and friendship of many famous men, including Senator Henry Clay and President Andrew Jackson.

While Father achieved many things, he is best remembered for his all-night ride through the woods on his mare Sally. It was one of the most heroic deeds in the history of our country. His journey that night was longer and more perilous than Paul Revere's famous ride.

So now — perhaps I have painted a portrait of my father after all!

Visit Jack Jouett's home:
Jack Jouett House Historic Site
255 Craig's Creek Road
Versailles, KY 40383
859.873.7902
www.jouetthouse.org